In the Beginning

In the Beginning

There was Joy

MATTHEW FOX

GODSFIELD PRESS

Once upon a time, time, time, time, time.

time

time

time

time

time

time

A long, long, long, long, long, long time ago.

long, long, long, long, long, long

long, long, long, long, long

long, long,

time ago.

Before there was time
  or times
or limes
or dimes
or even rhymes,

and before there was space, space, space, space, space.

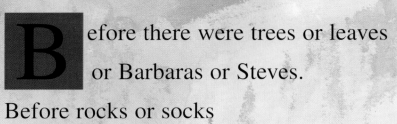

Before there were trees or leaves
or Barbaras or Steves.
Before rocks or socks
or violinists or jocks.
There was ... no thing.

There was Darkness among us.

Full, deep and dark, black, darkness.

No Space, no place, only darkness.

But what came before the darkness?
Before the darkness
There was Fun
on the run.
And Play
all day.

Fun

Play

And her name was ... Wisdom.

Wisdom and her maker
were named "Joy."

Mr. and Mrs. Joy to be exact.

Joy

Run

They played in the nothing
before there was something
and played with no thing.
They played with song
and sound
and round
and silence
and balance

and up

and in and out

and

down

and inside and outside

and downside and upside

upside
and down side.

One day Mrs. Joy sat down with Mr. Joy and said,

"Let's make a girl and a boy."

"What a great idea," said Mr. Joy.

"A girl Joy and a boy Joy –

to share our joy," said Mrs. Joy.

B ut Mr. Joy said,
"How shall we do this?
How shall we teach Boy Joy and Girl Joy to play?"

"There must be some day," Mrs. Joy said,
"for without the light, they will have no sight –
they will miss all the beauty
that so delights you and me.
So let's begin with light."

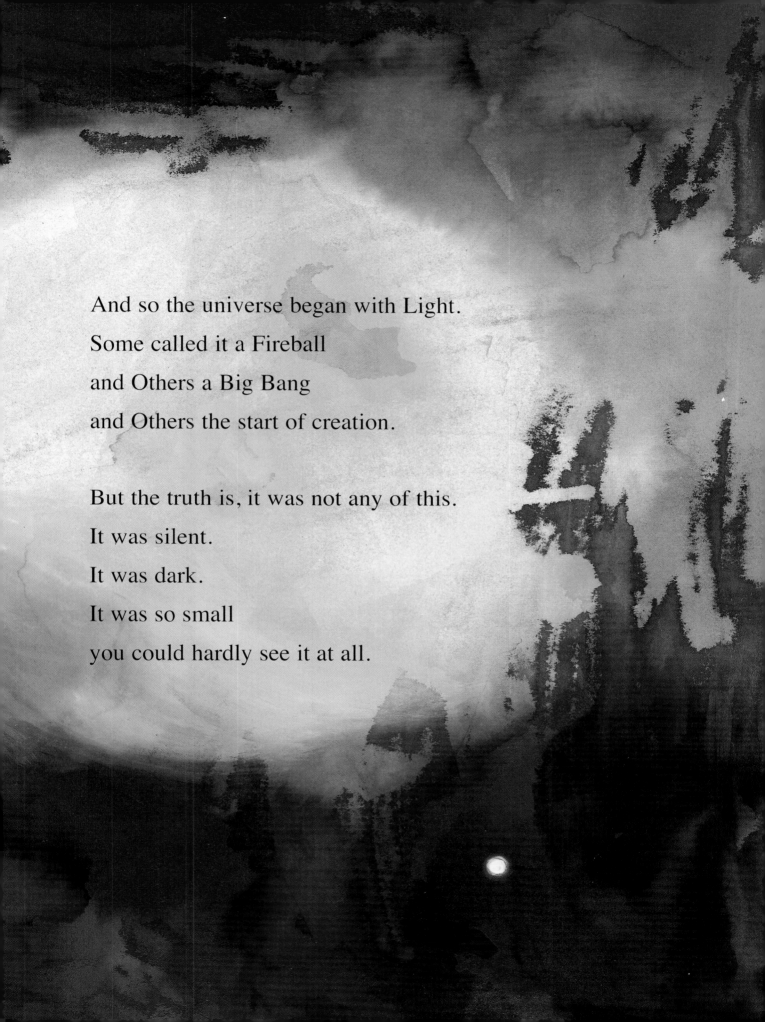

And so the universe began with Light.

Some called it a Fireball

and Others a Big Bang

and Others the start of creation.

But the truth is, it was not any of this.

It was silent.

It was dark.

It was so small

you could hardly see it at all.

I t was a mysterious fellow
that grew and grew
until one day – Whew!

It blew into a deep, silent, everywhere Yellow.

But to the Joy couple
things weren't yet just right.

"Where is the Joy?
Where is the boy?
Where is the girl Joy?"

They sat and sat
twirling their thinking cap.
They thought and thought –
"There's more we ought to do,
if our dream is to come true."

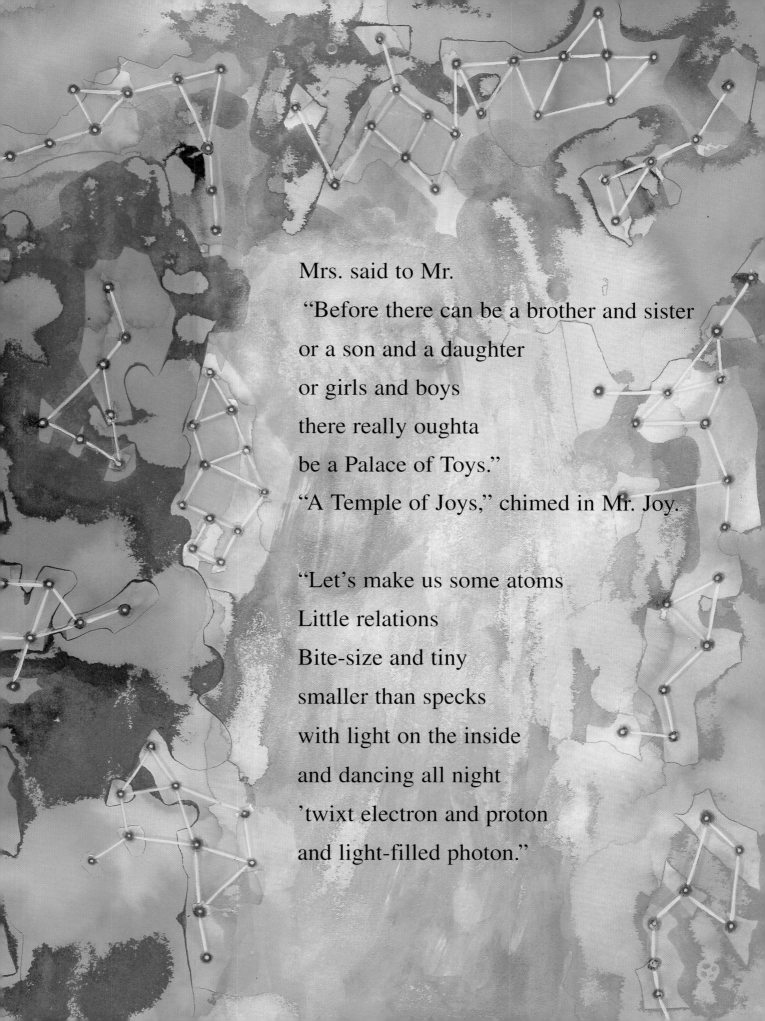

Mrs. said to Mr.
"Before there can be a brother and sister
or a son and a daughter
or girls and boys
there really oughta
be a Palace of Toys."
"A Temple of Joys," chimed in Mr. Joy.

"Let's make us some atoms
Little relations
Bite-size and tiny
smaller than specks
with light on the inside
and dancing all night
'twixt electron and proton
and light-filled photon."

"We'll build things of greatness,"
exclaimed his wife, Mrs. Joy.
"Galaxies and stars
and planets and moons
each playing its own tunes –
hurling, whirling, spinning out so far,
passing on the Light
even at Night."

"Supernovas, too,
who, when they explode with their colors,
will form planets and others
some cool and some hot
and some sunny and some not."

M r. Joy and his wife
were so overjoyed
and so happily employed,
so taken up in their plans
that they barely noticed
how the clock and its hands
had passed round and round
for billions of years.

"*Eikos*," they called it,
this home of their own
where all beings could roam
and expand as they might
and connect just right
into the ecology of things.

But back in their kitchen
the Joys were still fixin'
everything in order.

And now they were itchin'
to make their special invention
contrary to all convention
their biggest surprise ...
"a place we'll call earth,
for all of its worth,"
said Mrs. Joy.

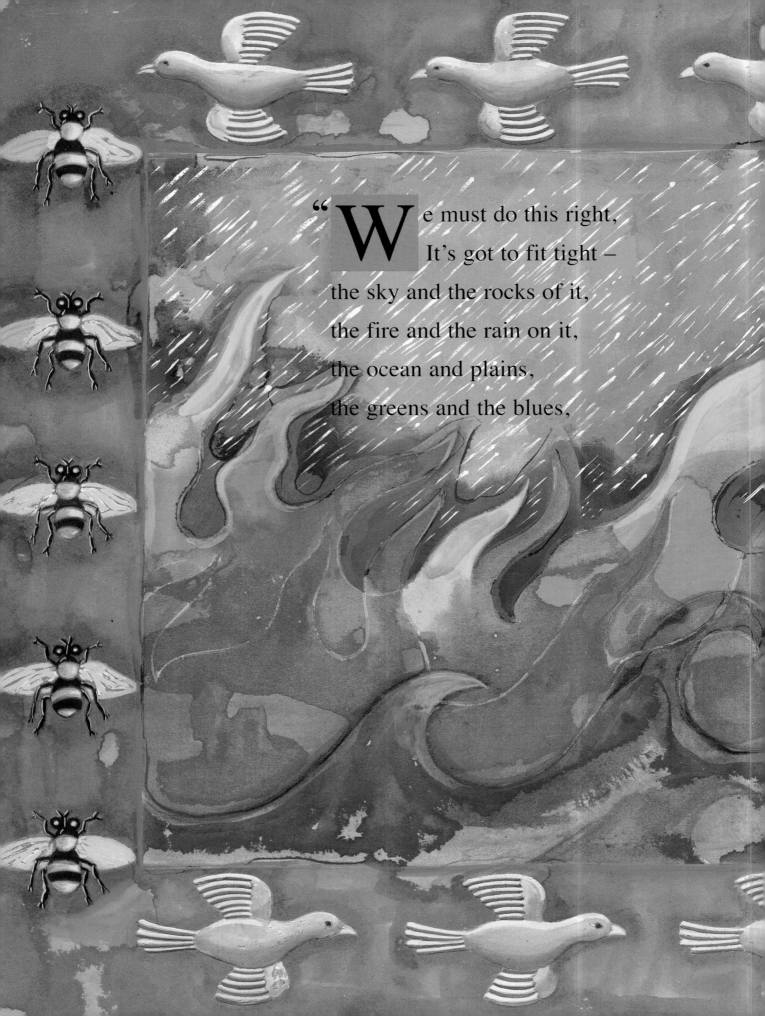

"We must do this right,
It's got to fit tight –
the sky and the rocks of it,
the fire and the rain on it,
the ocean and plains,
the greens and the blues,

the colors and the hues,
the woods and the trees,
the mosquitos and bees,
the birds and the songs,
the ozone and gongs.

The waters and lakes,
the desert that bakes,
the whales and worms,
the flowers and sperms,
the squirrels and doggies,

the wet and the soggies
all of it home
to the humans to come.
Yes! A place to delight in
where humans fit right in."

The ever-creative Joy couple continued their work:
"We'll make ears to hear sounds!

And eyes to taste colors!

Like orange and pink

and reds and yellers

fuccias and purples

and funnies and slurpples."

And skin to feel hot

and clothes when it's not

and noses to smell with

and hearts to swell with

love

and fun

and joy

and justice.

"Yes! There is no joy without justice," exclaimed Mrs. Joy.

love

fun

joy

justice

N ow we are ready,
  keep yourself steady,
– Don't scream.
It's time for the humans
to come on the scene.

A girl Joy and a boy Joy
Who will make children and grandchildren, too,

and do something new
with their space and their time,
with imaginations so fine
that we can hardly imagine
or fathom
or rhyme.

How shall we do this?
What will they look like?
What will they cook like?
What will they eat?
How will they sleep?
How special should they be?
How like you and me?

These were the questions
that occupied their sessions
when Mrs. and Mr. Joy
sat down to make humans.

They sat and they stuttered,
they moaned and they muttered,
they wondered and worried,
they felt themselves hurried.

Then Mr. Joy sat up with a start:
"What's all the fuss?
Let's make them like us."

"Like us?" asked Mrs. Joy.

"Yes! We'll give them art.
That would be amazing
their brains would be blazing
with images and fire
and cymbals and lyre
and poetry and art
they'll have a head start
if we make them like us."
And Mr. Joy thought:
"But there might also be trouble
and worry and strife

'cause if they are like us
they'll be creative and giving
and they'll have choices to make,
and the whole planet's at stake
if they mess things up."

"Yes, we're taking a risk,
that is for sure,"
offered Mrs. Joy as she shyly demured
and sipped at her coffee
dreaming the absurd.

What will guard the humans from wrong
    kinds of choices?
Where will they go to hear wisdom's voices?

What they must know is this
Eikos – our home – is precious with
its blues and its greens its valleys and sheens,
its water and forests and things that go "boraks"

in the middle of the night,

the frogs and the wombats,

the beavers and polecats,

the grains and the plains

and the fishes and tasty dishes.

The sun and the moon,
the planets and stars,
the woodchucks and frühstucks (breakfasts in Germany)
and puppies that are ours.
The kittens that purr,
the breezes that stir,
the air and the ozone,
the light and the dark zones,
all of it's a free zone
a place of grace.

We must tell our children this:
    your eyes and your ears and your nose and your tears
your singing and skipping, your belly-button and years –
all are a given;
a freebie; a grace.
That's what's so special about your time and your place.

Spirit is everywhere and everywhere still.
And love is unconditional
and there's forgiveness to boot!
All creation loves us
it all gives a hoot

about our past and our future
and your brother and sister
it's all blessing to you.
And me.
And us.

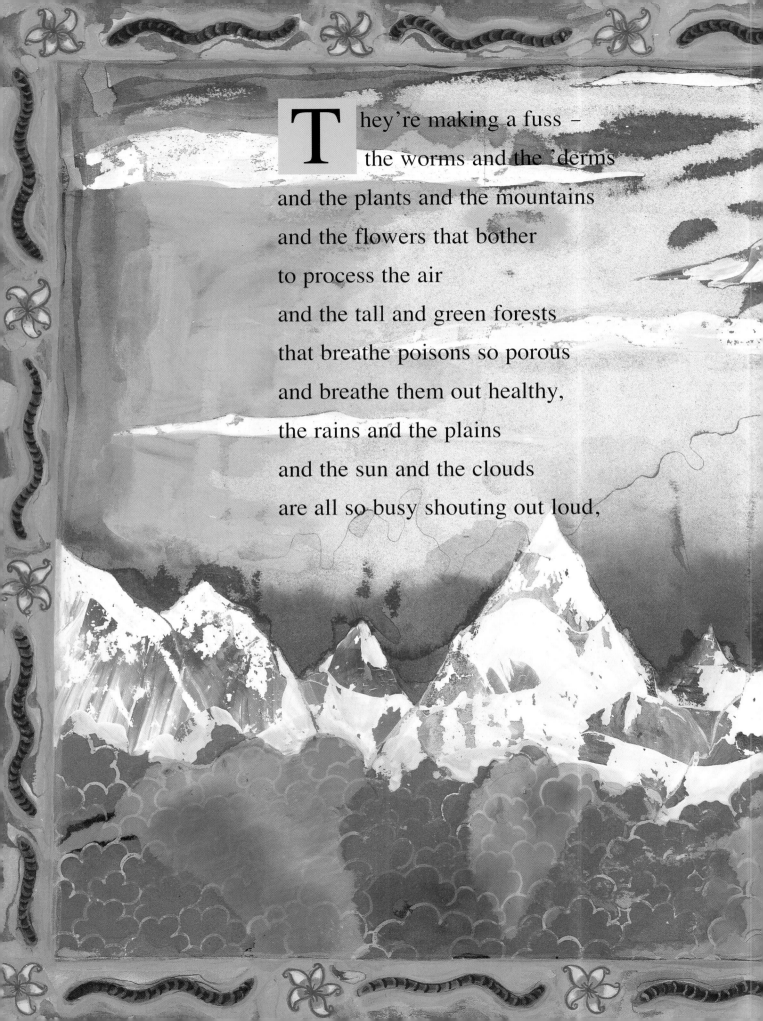

They're making a fuss –
the worms and the 'derms
and the plants and the mountains
and the flowers that bother
to process the air
and the tall and green forests
that breathe poisons so porous
and breathe them out healthy,
the rains and the plains
and the sun and the clouds
are all so busy shouting out loud,

"We love you,
we grace you,
we bless you."

These are the voices
that will help humans make choices
that cherish their planet
and all that is on it.

ut these voices have a question for humans as well:
        "Do you love us too?
do you think of us as we do you?
Do you live in a box
or do you love us rocks
as long and enduring
as we have loved you?"

"I bet," said Mrs. Joy,
"that our girl and our boy
will learn to enjoy
what is free and is gift,
what is grace and good,
that they will sift
the selfish from the shellfish,
the good from the bad,
the banal from the table,
the lazy from the able,
the dumb from the fun."

"Yes, indeed," said her husband.
"This is a risk worth taking,
making our children
in our image without faking.

They'll learn 'cause they must
what is beautiful and what is not,
what matters and what's rot.
And if they don't, it will all turn to dust."

So let's get on with it
we'll make them like us, then
sit back and enjoy it.
Surely these people will fit
into what we've been birthing
these fourteen billion years.
They will be happy,
funny and flappy.
They will find their way
remembering to say "Thank You" each day
for all this is gift and all that is grace,
for every place and every race
and every blade of grass and clover
and their legs that happily rover
over it all.

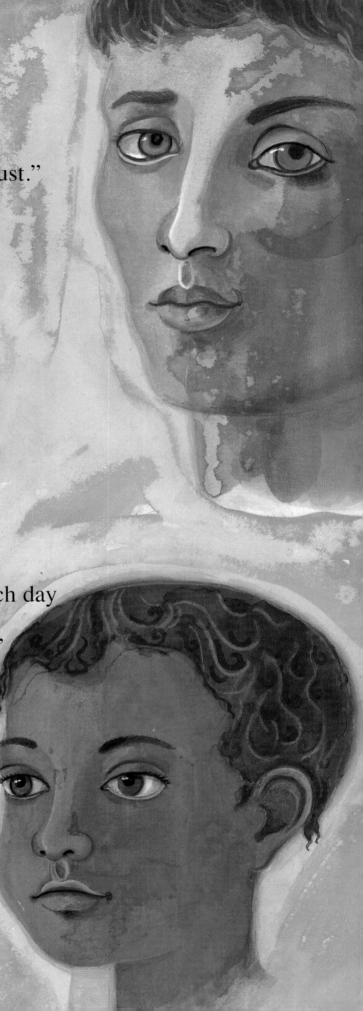

S urely they'll use their minds for peace,
their hearts for wonder,

their heads for thinking

and their anger for thunder. *Won't they?*

They will never turn to hating each other

or running down beauty

or emptying what's sooty

or making a mess

of their world that is the best

of just about everything we've made. *Would they?*

Surely, they will choose what is best

for themselves and their kids

and others to come

after they're gone. *Won't they?*

So let's sing the song

that begins a new creation.

Let's kiss the kiss

that gives humans recreation

and play all day

and fun on the run.

So, with lightning and thunder
amidst roses and doses
of loving and caring
we'll mold us a child
who's beautiful and wild
a truly, outstanding and beautiful wonder
– a Blessing, a good thing,
a new thing, a Whew! thing,
who can sing and loves dancing,
who can pray and do trancing,
a peace-maker, pace-maker,
clothes-maker, food-gatherer,
a lover, a worker, a burper,
a healer – a *grace*!
A mirror of our beauty
our laughter, our powers
that have made the world glitter
with oceans and flowers.
And we'll call these beings *"humans, children of Joy,"*
their smiling faces will shine
radiant and divine.

This instruction they gave the first girl and boy:
"Now heed this advice
if you want to find happiness and share what is nice:
When there is trouble
rise up from the rubble
and remember your origin and source of our name:

Joy is your heritage –
the family that made you –
give it and receive it
and don't ever leave it.
To Joy be true.
And never forget
to play every day.

Now and forever.
A holy endeavor.
Worlds without end.

Amen."

Acknowledgments

(in order of appearance):

The stars and rocks and supernovas and things

Genesis, chapters 1 and 2

Proverbs, chapter 8

THOMAS AQUINAS who wrote: "Sheer joy is God's and this demands companionship" and

"God has put a sheen into every being in the universe, a divine, luminous ray of light."

THOMAS BERRY and BRIAN SWIMME, *The Universe Story*

MEISTER ECKHART: "If the only prayer you say in your life is *'Thank You,'* that would suffice."

HILDEGARD OF BINGEN: "The entire world has been embraced by the Creator's Kiss."

The Song of Songs

Copyright © 1995 by *Godsfield Press*
Text © *Matthew Fox*
Illustrations © *Jane Tattersfield*
Originally published by *Godsfield Press Ltd 1995*
Designed by *The Bridgewater Book Company*

1 899434 65 8

 Write to

GODSFIELD PRESS LTD
Bowland House
off West Street, Alresford
Hants SO24 9AT

The right of Matthew Fox and Jane Tattersfield to be identified
as author and illustrator of this work has been asserted by them
in accordance with the Copyright, Designs and Patents Act 1988

A CIP catalogue record for this book is available from the British Library

Printed and bound in Singapore